S0-BIR-424

THIS BOOK BELONGS TO

____

and was completed on

____

WELCOME!

• • •

Hey guys! Welcome to the Smart Money Smart Kids *curriculum.*

I'm so excited to share this incredible class with you. These are the same principles that changed my life, and I believe they have the power to change the lives of you and your kids as well. For years, I've heard people say, "I wish I knew this stuff when I was younger." They see how managing God's money God's ways can have an impact on their lives, and they regret wasting years without using that approach.

Well, Smart Money Smart Kids *is here to change that, and I can't wait to see how it impacts you and your family!*

This Member Workbook has the opportunity to become ***a very special legacy piece*** *for you and your kids, so be sure to take advantage of every single writing exercise. You should bring this to class each week to accompany the video-based curriculum.*

Each lesson continues online, where Dad and I will teach you how to build character qualities in your kids that will set them up for success with money and in life. So make sure you register with the ***Activation Code found on your welcome letter*** *to get access to all the lessons.*

Thank you for taking this step, and I wish you the best!

• • •

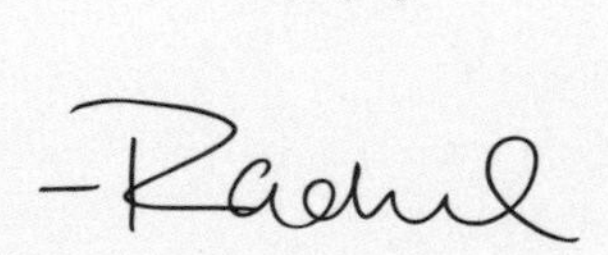

Table of Contents

1749 Mallory Lane • Brentwood, TN 37027

Published by The Lampo Group, Inc. For more information, please visit our website at daveramsey.com.

Meet Rachel and Dave

RACHEL CRUZE

Rachel Cruze is a seasoned communicator and presenter who has been speaking to groups as large as 10,000 for more than a decade. The daughter of Dave Ramsey, she uses the knowledge and experiences from growing up in the Ramsey household to educate America's students and young adults on the proper ways to handle money and stay out of debt. Her book *Smart Money Smart Kids,* co-authored by her dad, debuted at #1 on the *New York Times* best-sellers list.

• • •

*@RachelCruze * rachelcruze.com * facebook.com/rachelramseycruze*

DAVE RAMSEY

Dave Ramsey is America's trusted voice on money and business. More than 2.5 million families have attended *Financial Peace University* and *The Legacy Journey* classes in more than 45,000 churches nationwide. His nationally syndicated radio program, *The Dave Ramsey Show,* is heard by more than 8 million listeners each week on more than 550 radio stations throughout the United States. He's authored five *New York Times* best-selling books: *Financial Peace, More Than Enough, The Total Money Makeover, EntreLeadership,* and *Smart Money Smart Kids.*

• • •

*@DaveRamsey * daveramsey.com * facebook.com/daveramsey*

And whatever you do, do it heartily, as to the Lord and not to men

–COLOSSIANS 3:23

1 Lesson One
WORK AND RESPONSIBILITY

Remember the last time you felt that "good" kind of tired? You know, a tired that somehow creates exhaustion *and* satisfaction. That's the funny thing about work. It can be really hard, but it also gives us a sense of purpose like nothing else. We need that in our lives. And our kids need it in their lives too.

Work Is NOT a Four-Letter Word

This week, Rachel and Dave dive into the connection between work and money. They cover:

- How to help our kids find purpose in their work
- How work teaches them responsibility, gives them confidence, and prepares them for the real world
- And, most important, why work is an offering to God

• • •

Dave: The first group I ever spoke to about how to handle money was a Rotary Club with forty-three people in the audience. I used an overhead projector, and I actually had hair. That was a long time ago. When I finished my presentation that I had practiced hours for in front of a mirror, I walked to a table in the back of the room to sell copies of my little self-published book, *Financial Peace,* for twelve dollars each.

A middle-aged woman walked up to the book table, and I will never forget her comment. Holding my book, she looked at me and said, "Dave, that was great information. Why don't parents teach their children about money? Our kids need to know this information."

REFLECTION QUESTION

Take about two minutes to write your answer to the following question.

We all learned about handling money in different ways. Thinking back, what are one or two things that you remember learning from your parents?

Rachel: When I was in the fifth grade, I spent an afternoon at a friend's house and saw the weirdest thing. I watched my friend's mom clean her room, take our dishes to the sink after we ate, put her laundry away, feed the dog, and take out the trash, never once stopping to ask us to help. Right then, I knew my family was different.

I've learned so much from my parents over the years, but one of the most fundamental lessons they taught me from a young age was that the Ramseys are hard workers. People may know us for all of the products and services we offer, but if you're wondering what the Ramsey "family business" is, let me tell you from experience—the family business is *work*.

As an adult, I think back on my childhood and I'm extremely thankful for all my parents did for me. But there's one thing they taught me that I lean on literally every day of my life, and that's how to work. I learned early on that work creates discipline, and when you have discipline in your life, you are a healthier person.

WATCH: PART 1 17 minutes

It's time to hear more from Rachel and Dave about why work really isn't a four-letter word. Take a moment to watch the first part of Lesson One.

Video Notes and Thoughts:

Take about two minutes to write your answers to the following questions.

Rachel and Dave both talked about how important work was in the Ramsey home. Who taught you the importance of work? How did they do it?

"WORK, GET PAID; DON'T WORK, DON'T GET PAID.

—Dave Ramsey

Dave: I grew up in a wonderful *Leave It to Beaver* neighborhood, and our next-door neighbor was one of the nicest men I have ever known. He would help anyone in need, but he was also a mechanical genius who loved fixing things. To accomplish his hobbies, he collected stuff in his backyard—I mean, a lot of stuff.

Every so often, all the neighborhood kids and many of the adults would show up and help John clean up his backyard. We worked for hours, moving scrap metal, filling trucks with things to be hauled to the dump, and mowing and trimming the yard. When the yard was finally clean, all the kids jumped in the back of John's pickup truck for a ride down to the Kwik Sak™ for an ICEE™.

I look back on the lessons those mornings taught me: hard work, working with others, and, of course, repaying the kindness of a helpful neighbor with a simple cleanup day. Those neighborhood work days played a huge role in making me the man I am today.

WATCH: PART 2 8 minutes

Join Rachel as she explains how parents can use work to teach their kids important lessons about responsibility.

Video Notes and Thoughts:

REFLECTION  QUESTION

Take about two minutes to write your answer to the following question.

At the end of the video, Rachel talked about the importance of finding purpose in your work. As you think about what you do for a living, how do you find purpose in your work?

***SIGN IN** TO SMARTMONEYSMARTKIDS.COM

Join Rachel and Dave as they discuss the importance of helping our children understand the connection between work and money.

****IMPORTANT:** If you haven't registered yet, you will need the **Activation Code** included on the welcome letter in your kit.*

Deep Dives

This lesson's Deep Dives section helps you teach your kids about the satisfaction that comes from earning money. It includes age-specific exercises, videos, and activities that match your kids' life stages.

Rachel: Without fail, every time I'm on the road speaking to groups, I have parents ask me, "How can I raise my kids not to feel entitled? How can I teach them the value of a dollar?" From my experience, the basic principle of working is one of the best ways to combat the attitude of entitlement. Once your kids understand that money comes from work, they won't be able to spend money without considering how much work went into actually *making* the money.

REFLECTION  QUESTION

Take a few minutes to write your responses to the following statement.

Before watching the Deep Dive Overview, think about how each of your kids relates to work and money. Using the scale below, mark where you think each of them falls in terms of understanding where money comes from.

____
NAME 1

① • ② • ③ • ④ • ⑤ • ⑥ • ⑦ • ⑧ • ⑨ • ⑩
PARENTS' POCKET **HARD WORK**

____
NAME 2

① • ② • ③ • ④ • ⑤ • ⑥ • ⑦ • ⑧ • ⑨ • ⑩
PARENTS' POCKET **HARD WORK**

____
NAME 3

① • ② • ③ • ④ • ⑤ • ⑥ • ⑦ • ⑧ • ⑨ • ⑩
PARENTS' POCKET **HARD WORK**

____
NAME 4

① • ② • ③ • ④ • ⑤ • ⑥ • ⑦ • ⑧ • ⑨ • ⑩
PARENTS' POCKET **HARD WORK**

WATCH: DEEP DIVE OVERVIEW

Join Rachel and Dave as they share some practical handles for teaching your kids the biblical principles behind work.

APPLICATION: DEEP DIVES

Age-Specific Application

The next three pages contain age-specific videos and activities. **Please skip to the section(s) that best fits your family.**

Younger Children *(AGES 3-5)*

Rachel: I've talked to many parents who tried the commission system with their younger children. Even at three or four years old, kids will jump on board with new things—yes, even money-type things—quicker than you may realize. You can create incredible teachable moments when you give your young children an opportunity to do a few things around the house and get paid for doing them.

WATCH: AGES 3–5 DEEP DIVE

Join Rachel and Dave as they talk about some simple steps you can take to help your preschooler make the connection between work and money.

PUTTING IT INTO PRACTICE

List three simple chores that your child can do right now to earn money:

1. Food and water for Watson
2. cleaning room
3. Set the table / unload dishwasher

FAMILY ACTIVITIES

Make sure you do the family activity found in the online experience, and be prepared to discuss it during the next class. Also remember to look for teachable moments throughout the week.

CONVERSATION STARTER

Ask your kids what they want to buy with the money they earn from their commissions. Write what they say in the space below. You are sure to get some memorable responses!

huge lego set

Older Children *(AGES 6–13)*

Rachel: As your children grow, the chore responsibilities—and maybe even the dollar amounts—should grow to reflect their ability and maturity. As I got older, I wanted to do more things and buy more stuff, just like any other kid. That meant that as my wants and needs grew, so did my list of chores.

WATCH: AGES 6–13 DEEP DIVE

Join Rachel and Dave as they discuss how older kids can start processing ideas like delayed gratification and the envelope system.

PUTTING IT INTO PRACTICE

Use the chart below to decide what chores your kids will do for commissions (and how much each chore will pay) and what chores they will do simply because they are part of the family:

Commission Chores	Family Chores
Take out the garbage	*Clean the dishes*

FAMILY ACTIVITIES

Make sure you do the family activity found in the online experience, and be prepared to discuss it during the next class. Also remember to look for teachable moments throughout the week.

CONVERSATION STARTER

Ask your kids to describe the difference between the Give, Save, and Spend envelopes. Ask them how having three envelopes—instead of just one—will help them manage their money better. Write what they say below.

Teenage Children *(AGES 14-COLLEGE)*

Rachel: Teens should always share the chores around the house. But if Mom and Dad are the only "bosses" kids know, they won't have a chance to learn other important lessons about working for—and with—other people. When I was a junior in high school, I worked at the local mall during the Christmas season. That's when I learned about filling out W-2 forms, filing taxes every year, and experiencing the crushing heartache of having the government take a quarter of my paycheck in taxes and Social Security. Those are great lessons for your teens to learn by working outside the home.

WATCH: AGES 14–COLLEGE DEEP DIVE

Join Rachel and Dave as they reflect on the value of getting a job in the "real world"—either as an entrepreneur or by working for someone else.

PUTTING IT INTO PRACTICE

Memorize Colossians 3:23 this week: "And whatever you do, do it heartily, as to the Lord and not to men." (You can encourage your kids to memorize this verse too!)

How well do you live out this verse? What example are you setting for your kids? Write your thoughts below.

FAMILY ACTIVITIES

Make sure you do the family activity found in the online experience, and be prepared to discuss it during the next class. Also remember to look for teachable moments throughout the week.

CONVERSATION STARTER

Ask your kids what kind of jobs they are interested in and why. It will be fun to see how this ends up being different from their future careers, so be sure to write what they say below.

REFLECTION

What's Your Money Story?

Rachel and Dave both told their unique money stories. Take a few minutes to reflect on your personal money stories, then capture them in the space below.

How would you describe your family's financial situation when you were growing up?

What were some of the first things you did to earn money. How much did those jobs pay?

What types of financial challenges have you faced?

REFLECTION

What financial accomplishments are you really proud of?

If you could teach your kids anything from your experience with money, what would it be?

NEXT WEEK

Be prepared to discuss what you've learned from this week's lesson or to share your experiences with teachable moments this week.

Train up a child in the way he should go, and when he is old he will not depart from it.

–PROVERBS 22:6

2

Lesson Two

SPENDING AND WISDOM

As parents, it's our job to guide our kids toward wisdom in every area of life—including the way they handle their money. And since we live in the most marketed-to culture in history, it's especially important that we teach our kids to spend wisely so they can win as adults.

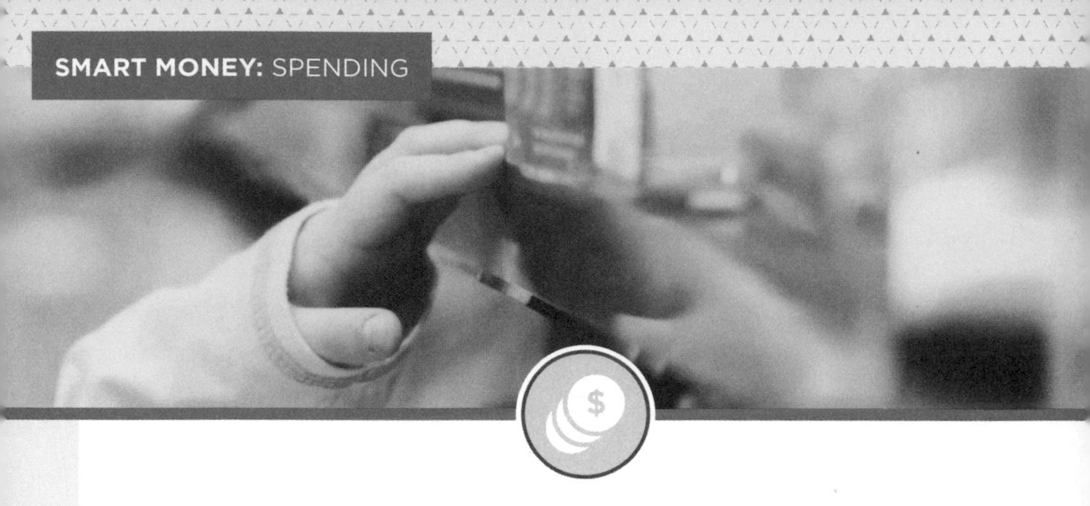

When It's Gone, It's Gone

In this lesson, Rachel tackles the topic of spending. She covers:

- Why kids need to learn how to spend, not just save
- How to help kids play to their own strengths—whether they are spenders or savers
- Why it's our job to guide our kids toward wisdom

• • •

Rachel: Money is finite. There is not an infinite supply. That's something a lot of people have trouble remembering these days. In a time when crazy mortgages, car loans, student loans, and credit cards make you believe *anyone* can purchase *anything* at *any time* with no consequences, it's easy to forget that money has limits. Whether your children are six years old at an amusement park or fifty-six years old at a car dealership, they will never win with money until they understand that money can—and often does—run out.

REFLECTION QUESTION

Take about two minutes to write your answers to the following questions.

Has there ever been a time in your life, whether as a kid or an adult, when the money ran out? What happened?

Rachel: I firmly believe that a lot of people make huge, expensive mistakes as adults simply because they were never allowed to make small, inexpensive mistakes when they were kids. Many parents try so hard to protect their children from the pain of hard lessons that they never develop the wisdom and toughness that only come by experiencing failure.

Mom and Dad were great in these situations. They had a balanced response, and they let me make mistakes and learn from them.

WATCH: PART 1 13 minutes

It's time to hear more from Rachel about teaching money-smart kids how to spend wisely. Take a few minutes to watch the first part of Lesson Two.

Thoughts and Notes:

only spend the money you have
raise up a child in the way he is bent

REFLECTION QUESTION

Take about two minutes to write your answer to the following question.

Rachel talked about how important it is for us to lead our kids based on how they are naturally wired. Think about your children. What unique strengths do you see in each of them?

Oliver is a spender. He values the things he buys.
Sam is less concerned with things.

"MONEY IS FUN...IF YOU'VE GOT SOME!

–Dave Ramsey

Dave: It takes tremendous strength and resolve to allow your kids to suffer the consequences of their decisions. They are persuasive, cute, and pushy, so it is really tough not to cave and say to yourself, *Well, they are only children.* Certainly there were plenty of times we intentionally bailed out a child who made a dumb mistake. But there were equally as many times when Sharon and I knew if we permitted them to fail while the outcome was under our control, we could keep our hand on the pain thermostat, allowing the temperature to get hot enough to teach the lesson, but not so hot as to do permanent damage.

When you run out of money, no amount of cuteness, whining, pouting, or persuasion changes the math. You are still broke. And you are broke because you did not control your spending. I meet fifty-four-year-olds who still have not learned this simple lesson.

WATCH: PART 2 8 minutes

Join Rachel as she shares tips for overcoming the pressures of our culture and raising kids who can make wise spending choices.

Thoughts and Notes

Social media
our kids need wisdom to navigate

experience leads to understanding, then that leads to wisdom

ask God to help you pass on wisdom.
They can ask Him for wisdom.

wait, sleep on it, see if you still want it in the morning

REFLECTION  QUESTION

Take about two minutes to write your answer to the following question.

In what ways do you see marketing and social media making an impact on your kids' lives?

Buy nothing groups

SIGN IN TO SMARTMONEYSMARTKIDS.COM

Join Rachel and Dave as they discuss how letting kids feel the weight of small money failures while they are still under your roof can lead to big financial wins later.

Deep Dives

Money-smart kids make wise spending decisions—and this lesson's Deep Dives section offers some practical tips for leading your kids toward those good choices. It includes age-specific exercises, videos, and activities that match your kids' life stages.

Dave: Your example is *everything* when teaching your children about money. How many of us as parents have opened our mouths and our mothers' or fathers' words have come out? Your children are going to become a lot like you, so to the extent that you want them to win with money, you better get about the business of winning with money.

Your kids will spend like you, save like you, give like you, budget like you, and fight with their spouses about money . . . like you.

REFLECTION  QUESTION

Take about two minutes to write your answer to the following question.

Good or bad, what is something that you remember your mom or dad specifically saying about money?

WATCH: DEEP DIVE OVERVIEW

Join Rachel and Dave as they talk about how feeling the weight of financial decisions can help kids learn to make wise spending choices.

APPLICATION: DEEP DIVES

Age-Specific Application

The next three pages contain age-specific videos and activities. **Please skip to the section(s) that best fits your family.**

Younger Children *(AGES 3-5)*

Rachel: I really want to stress the fact that there's nothing right about being a saver, and there's nothing wrong with being a spender. Neither is better or worse than the other. But it is important to figure out which type of money personality your child has and direct him toward wise decisions and money habits.

WATCH: AGES 3–5 DEEP DIVE

Join Rachel and Dave as they talk about how letting preschoolers spend their own money helps them make the emotional connection between earning money and spending money.

PUTTING IT INTO PRACTICE

Show your preschooler a penny, nickel, and dime. Ask them which one is more valuable. (Often kids will pick the nickel because it's bigger.) Take a few minutes to explain the value of each coin, and write down what happened below.

FAMILY ACTIVITIES

Make sure you do the family activity found in the online experience, and be prepared to discuss it during the next class. Also remember to look for teachable moments throughout the week.

CONVERSATION STARTER

Ask your kid some basic money questions, like: How many nickels or dimes does it take to equal one dollar? *Be sure to write what they say in the space below.*

Older Children *(AGES 6–13)*

Rachel: *Opportunity cost* is one of those fancy financial terms that some people choke on. Let me make it easy for you: If you spend all your money on X, you can't also spend that money on Y. This one is pretty easy to explain to your kids. Use an example they care about, such as, "If you buy this video game today, you won't have the money to buy the new game that comes out next month."

WATCH: AGES 6–13 DEEP DIVE

Join Rachel and Dave as they talk about how letting kids make mistakes while they are still under your roof can save them from bigger problems down the road.

PUTTING IT INTO PRACTICE

During a trip to the grocery store, give your kids a list of three or four items and encourage them to find the best bargain for each. After they've made their selections, talk about why one item can be offered at many different prices, and explain how you decide which brand to buy.

FAMILY ACTIVITIES

Make sure you do the family activity found in the online experience, and be prepared to discuss it during the next class. Also remember to look for teachable moments throughout the week.

CONVERSATION STARTER

Ask your older child(ren) this question: If you wanted two things but only had the money for one, how would you choose between them? *Write their response in the space below.*

Teenage Children *(AGES 14-COLLEGE)*

Rachel: One of the best ways to avoid a bad purchase is to simply wait overnight. Regardless of how young or old you are, waiting overnight before making a big purchase completely changes the buying decision. Show your kids that waiting overnight takes the pressure off. It gives you permission to leave the store without the item, and once you leave the store, you often feel like a fog lifts from your mind and you can think clearly again.

WATCH: AGES 14–COLLEGE DEEP DIVE

Join Rachel and Dave as they discuss the importance of moving your teens from the envelope system to a zero-based budget.

PUTTING IT INTO PRACTICE

Ask your teen to read the story of the man building a tower in Luke 14:28–30. Have a conversation about why having a plan for spending money is so important, and help them fill out a zero-based budget. (You can download our forms for free at smartmoneysmartkids.com.)

FAMILY ACTIVITIES

Make sure you do the family activity found in the online experience, and be prepared to discuss it during the next class. Also remember to look for teachable moments throughout the week.

CONVERSATION STARTER

Talk with your teenager about why God seems to care so much about the way we handle money. Ask them if His level of interest surprises them—and why. Write the highlights from this conversation in the space below.

Learning to Spend Wisely

We have all had unique experiences when it comes to how we learned to spend money. Take a few minutes to write your reflections in the spaces below.

Was there a particular person who modeled the art of spending money wisely for you? If so, how did they do that?

We've all made purchases that we later regretted. What are one or two unwise purchases that you've made over the years?

What wise spending habits do you really want to pass on to your children?

REFLECTION

In what area of spending do you want to improve for the sake of your kids?

Why is it important to you that you learn and live out smart money habits and pass them on to your kids?

NEXT WEEK

Be prepared to discuss what you've learned from this week's lesson or to share your experiences with teachable moments this week.

For the love of money is a root of all kinds of evil

–1 TIMOTHY 6:10

3 *Lesson Three* SAVING AND PATIENCE

Saving doesn't come naturally to a lot of people, but spenders need to learn how to save—just like savers need to learn how to spend. The key to making it happen is pretty simple: it's mostly about behavior. When it comes to raising money-smart kids, teaching them to save not only instills patience, but it also builds their character!

Learning to Wait for It

This week, Rachel and Dave talk about why learning to save is such an important skill for our kids to master. They cover:

- How saving teaches our kids patience and keeps them from feeling entitled
- What makes saving different from hoarding
- And why kids who are natural savers need your help setting goals

• • •

Rachel: In the last lesson, we focused on spending. That's pretty much the starting point for kids and money. Being able to go into a store and spend their own money is the most powerful way to reinforce the work-money connections we talked about in Lesson One.

But if we stop there, we've got a huge problem. Four-year-olds can get by with the work-money-toy cash-flow system; grown-ups can't. If we want to raise young men and women who win with money, we've got to teach them to save.

Take about two minutes to write your answers to the following questions.

What are two or three things you've saved up for over a long period of time? How long did it take? Why was that particular purchase worth the wait?

Dave: When you teach your child proper spending, saving, and giving behaviors until those behaviors become character traits, you are ensuring the future success of your child. When a kid saves money, it is not a mathematical event; it is a maturity event that gives dignity.

When a kid buys something with money he or she has saved, it is not merely a financial transaction; you are watching poise, confidence, and maturity develop right before your eyes. When you grow great behaviors and character traits in your children, you are really teaching them how to win at life.

WATCH: PART 1 10 minutes

It's time to hear more from Rachel and Dave about why saving money is such a big deal. Take a few minutes to watch the first part of Lesson Three.

Video Notes and Thoughts:

REFLECTION  QUESTION

Take about two minutes to write your answer to the following question.

As a natural spender, Rachel talked about how her pursuit of a car helped her learn to save. Are you naturally a spender or a saver? Talk about an event in your life that helped you see the value of both.

“

YOU HAVE THE POWER TO CHANGE YOUR FAMILY TREE!

–Rachel Cruze

SMART KIDS: PATIENCE

Rachel: Kids aren't always naturally patient people. Shocking, I know. One of the most terrifying moments for many parents is getting to a restaurant and hearing, "There's a forty-five-minute wait." When you're five, forty-five minutes is an eternity!

However, those moments—as painful as they can be for kids *and* parents—are important. They teach children how to wait for something fun, and that's a huge lesson in today's world.

WATCH: PART 2 7 minutes

Join Rachel as she talks about the power of delayed gratification and how teaching patience can help parents raise money-smart kids.

Video Notes and Thoughts:

REFLECTION  QUESTION

Take about two minutes to write your answers to the following questions.

Imagine that your kids are all grown up and they have developed the identical level of patience to save money as you have right now. How does that make you feel? What are some things you might want to change about yourself?

SIGN IN TO SMARTMONEYSMARTKIDS.COM

Join Rachel and Dave as they discuss finding balance between saving and spending and how to combat the culture of instant gratification.

Deep Dives

Patience may be a virtue, but it's certainly not easy—especially when you can spend your money instead of save it! But today's Deep Dives section offers some practical ideas for teaching kids how to save money with patience. It includes age-specific exercises, videos, and activities that match your kids' life stages.

Rachel: Learning how and why to save money is one of the most fundamental financial disciplines there is. I can't think of a better way to set your child up for lifelong success than to simply teach him how to save.

It's not always easy, and it certainly isn't always fun. But knowing how to save, delay gratification, set goals and priorities, make huge purchases with cash instead of debt, cover emergencies, and prepare for long-term investing is critical for any young man or woman leaving home for the first time. These are all lessons you can teach your children today, no matter how old they are or where you're starting from.

REFLECTION  QUESTION

Take about two minutes to complete the following activity.

Write each of your kids' names below, and talk about why you think they are a natural spender or a saver.

WATCH: DEEP DIVE OVERVIEW

Join Rachel and Dave as they talk about specific ways to encourage your kids to save wisely—no matter how they are bent.

Age-Specific Application

The next three pages contain age-specific videos and activities. **Please skip to the section(s) that best fits your family.**

Younger Children *(AGES 3-5)*

Rachel: When delayed gratification becomes a part of your personality, you understand that you can't have everything you want right when you want it. This is a great lesson to learn early in life.

WATCH: AGES 3-5 DEEP DIVE

Join Rachel and Dave as they discuss the value of teaching your kids early on that saving money is just as important as spending it.

PUTTING IT INTO PRACTICE

Ask your preschooler to name one thing they'd like to buy with their own money. Work together to find out how much the item will cost.

Then make a savings chart that divides the cost into four or five roughly equal parts. This could be a pie chart, a thermometer, or any other fun image that allows you to track progress toward the goal. Every time your kids reach a savings milestone on the chart, let them color a section of the chart.

When the chart is filled, count out the money and head for the store. Use this as a teachable moment—and heap on the praise for a job well done!

FAMILY ACTIVITIES

Make sure you do the family activity found in the online experience, and be prepared to discuss it during the next class. Also remember to look for teachable moments throughout the week.

CONVERSATION STARTER

Ask your kids why they think it's a good idea to save some money instead of spending it all. Talk about the role of patience in saving and why it might be a hard quality to develop. Write their responses in the space below.

Older Children *(AGES 6–13)*

Rachel: My dad has always taught that people need to save for three reasons: first, an emergency fund, then purchases, and then wealth building. I completely agree with that, but when you're dealing with children, you need to change up the order a bit.

Like we've said, the best opportunity you'll have to start teaching your young children about money is in their purchases. So that's where we'll start.

WATCH: AGES 6–13 DEEP DIVE

Join Rachel and Dave as they talk about the process of teaching kids to set savings goals—and why you should celebrate with your kids when those goals are met.

PUTTING IT INTO PRACTICE

Ask your kids: Would you rather receive one million dollars now or a penny doubled every day for thirty days? Then ask why. Show them the "Penny Saved" chart below. Show them how saving and doubling pennies every day actually ends up being $5.3 million—way more than a lump sum of $1 million!

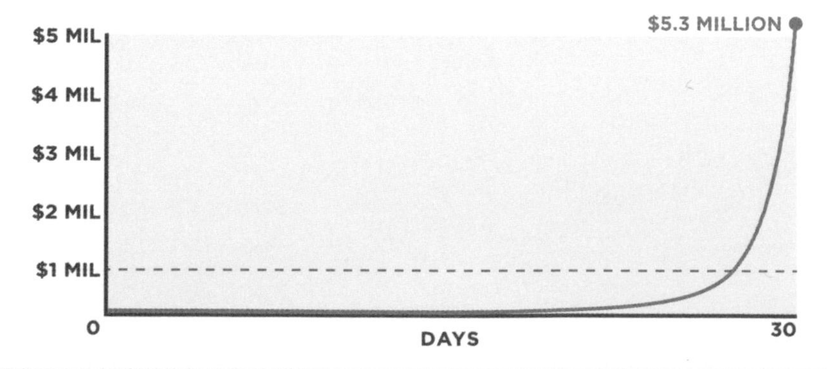

FAMILY ACTIVITIES

Make sure you do the family activity found in the online experience, and be prepared to discuss it during the next class. Also remember to look for teachable moments throughout the week.

CONVERSATION STARTER

Older kids can make the transition from clear jars to three envelopes: Give, Save, and Spend. Ask your child how much should go into each envelope each week and why. Remember to emphasize that all three envelopes are important! Record the highlights from this conversation in the space below.

Teenage Children *(AGES 14-COLLEGE)*

Rachel: Teenagers have a whole new set of savings goals. Sure, they're still buying some "toys," but those look more like electronic gadgets or purses. On top of that, the normal expenses of teenage life begin to resemble adult life. They start going out with their friends, going out on dates, buying gas, paying cell phone bills, and generally needing more money.

Your kids are growing up—and so are their financial needs. That means it's time to get more focused and intentional than ever about saving money.

WATCH: AGES 14–COLLEGE DEEP DIVE

Join Rachel and Dave as they talk about why teens need to think about saving for emergencies and for the bigger buys like cars and college.

PUTTING IT INTO PRACTICE

Read Proverbs 6:6–8 with your teenager. Explain that ants are wise to store things up during good times so they will have what they need during not-so-good times. Encourage your teen to think about a few situations when they would be glad to have some money saved up. Talk about why that's important and use this as a teachable moment to share the importance of an emergency fund.

FAMILY ACTIVITIES

Make sure you do the family activity found in the online experience, and be prepared to discuss it during the next class. Also remember to look for teachable moments throughout the week.

CONVERSATION STARTER

Ask your teen: How much money would you like to have in your emergency fund? Why did you pick that amount? *(Parent note: Rachel and Dave recommend at least $500 for a teenager's emergency fund.) Write your teen's answers to these questions in the space below.*

REFLECTION

Your Story of Saving

Dave said that the art of saving is a primitive concept with profound results. Take a few minutes to reflect a little bit on your savings story and respond to the following questions.

Think way back. What is the very first thing you can remember intentionally saving up money for? How much was it?

What's the biggest thing that you have ever saved up and paid cash for? How did it feel?

What about now? What kinds of things are you actively saving for at the moment?

REFLECTION

What life advice would you give to your "natural saver" child?

What about your "natural spender" child? What advice would you give to them?

NEXT WEEK

Be prepared to discuss what you've learned from this week's lesson or to share your experiences with teachable moments this week.

For God so loved the world that He gave His one and only Son that whoever believes in him shall not perish but have eternal life

–JOHN 3:16 (NIV)

4

Lesson Four

GIVING AND GENEROSITY

The last thing that any of us want our kids to be is selfish. In today's lesson, Rachel and Dave reveal how teaching our kids the act of giving leads to generosity—the antidote to selfishness!

It's Not Yours Anyway

This week, Rachel and Dave discuss some really important principles related to giving. They cover how:

- Giving reminds kids that God owns it all
- Generosity helps kids focus on the needs of others
- Giving is about more than just money—it makes us more like Christ

• • •

Dave: As far back as I can remember, I have been driven to reach certain goals. My parents gave me the wonderful gift of believing I could do anything I set my mind to if I only worked hard enough. So as a young man, I set my mind to the gathering of "stuff." Making money was simply a means for me to live the good life, because, after all, it *was* all about me.

Then in my early twenties, I met God. I met Him in a radical, life-changing way, and after He entered my life, He began reshaping my selfish heart into the heart of a giver. He has been working on that young selfish guy ever since.

REFLECTION QUESTION

Take about two minutes to write your answers to the following questions.

Have you ever had a life-changing experience like Dave did in his early twenties? If so, what changes did you see in yourself?

Rachel: As I travel across the country speaking to teens, I meet a lot of sweet, responsible, hard-working kids. But I have encountered a lot of self-centered ones, as well. Having a selfish mentality is a big obstacle for a lot of people. It's definitely something your kids either already struggle with or will face one day. That's because they are growing up in a culture that is obsessed with "me, me, me."

I'm not saying every young person in America is selfish and greedy, but let's face it: the act of giving isn't always the first thing they think about. But when your kids grow up in a house where giving is a priority, they start to see *themselves* differently because they see *other people* differently.

WATCH: PART 1 11 minutes

It's time to hear more from Rachel about why giving needs to be a big part of our kids' lives. Take a few minutes to watch the first part of Lesson Four.

Video Notes and Thoughts:

REFLECTION  QUESTION

Take about two minutes to write your answer to the following question.

Rachel talked about living in a "bubble" until her mom encouraged her to take two girls shopping. What kind of bubble are your kids currently living in?

GIVING IS AN ACT. GENEROSITY IS AN ATTITUDE.

—Rachel Cruze

Dave: Sharon and I have always looked for opportunities that were part of everyday life to teach our children hands-on lessons about money. Sometimes, if the teachable moment did not occur naturally, we would manufacture a moment or an event.

For instance, there were a couple of years we modeled giving by choosing an angel from the "Angel Tree," a program that provided Christmas presents for kids who have a parent in prison. As Sharon and I took our kids to find the perfect gift for our angel, sometimes the only results were three whiny kids who argued to buy something for themselves and two frustrated parents who were appalled at their selfish offspring. Not exactly the intended spirit. But we regularly looked for bubble-bursting moments because they helped create gratefulness in our children.

WATCH: PART 2 7 minutes

Join Rachel as she talks about generosity and how a giving spirit sets kids up for success in the future.

Video Notes and Thoughts:

REFLECTION  QUESTION

Take about two minutes to write your answer to the following question.

Rachel reminded us that we are blessed to be a blessing. What are some blessings God has given your family that you are especially thankful for?

GO ONLINE

Join Rachel and Dave as they discuss giving as the antidote for selfishness and how parents can encourage generosity in the lives of their kids.

Deep Dives

We live in a pretty materialistic world, and that sense of selfishness can rub off on our kids. But today's Deep Dives section takes a look at how we can move our kids from feelings of entitlement to a mindset of generosity, where they are focused on meeting the needs of others. It includes videos and activities that are relevant to your kid's ages.

Rachel: I truly believe more is caught than taught—that what your kids *see you do* is a lot more powerful than what they *hear you say*. Words can be strong, but actions are stronger. The strongest impact on children, though, is when they hear and see a consistent message from their parents. When the parents' words and actions come together, it forms a powerful statement about that family's value system.

Many parents miss this opportunity, not because they aren't giving, but because they aren't being intentional about letting their kids *see* them give. Help them make the mental and emotional connection between money and the people it's going to help.

REFLECTION  QUESTION

Take about two minutes to write your answers to the following questions.

What really inspires and motivates you to give? How can you help your kids share the joy of giving in these moments?

SIGN IN TO SMARTMONEYSMARTKIDS.COM

Join Rachel and Dave as they discuss the biblical basis for giving and why your kids need to make it a part of their daily lives.

Age-Specific Application

The next three pages contain age-specific videos and activities. **Please skip to the section(s) that best fits your family.**

Younger Children *(AGES 3-5)*

Rachel: While this won't be true 100 percent of the time in every family, I do believe little kids have more of a free spirit when it comes to giving. Maybe they haven't yet learned to hold money tightly the way the world eventually warns them to do. So, when your children are young, encourage that spirit of giving and sharing. Do whatever you can to keep that childlike spirit alive!

WATCH: AGES 3–5 DEEP DIVE

Join Rachel and Dave as they talk about how emphasizing the value of sharing can lead your preschooler toward a life of generous giving.

PUTTING IT INTO PRACTICE

Read the story of the little boy who shared the loaves and fish with Jesus (John 6:1-13). Talk about why sharing is important, and encourage your kids to find ways they can share with people in need. Make plans to complete one of your preschooler's ideas this week.

FAMILY ACTIVITIES

Make sure you do the family activity found in the online experience, and be prepared to discuss it during the next class. Also remember to look for teachable moments throughout the week.

CONVERSATION STARTER

Ask your child the following question: Why does God like it when we share with others? *Write your child's response in the space below.*

Older Children *(AGES 6-13)*

Rachel: Around age six, I started putting my own dollar in the red velvet offering bag as it passed by. That was such a great experience for me. Too often, parents just give their child a dollar as they walk into church each week. When that happens, the child isn't really giving anything—he's just a little deliveryman for the parents' money. There's not an emotional connection between working for the money and choosing to give it away.

WATCH: AGES 6–13 DEEP DIVE

Join Rachel and Dave as they share why teaching kids to give their own money is just as important as teaching them to spend their own money.

PUTTING IT INTO PRACTICE

Rachel says that money is like a magnifying glass—it makes you more of what you already are. Ask your kids to name some people they think are really generous. List a few ways those folks show their generosity:

FAMILY ACTIVITIES

Make sure you do the family activity found in the online experience, and be prepared to discuss it during the next class. Also remember to look for teachable moments throughout the week.

CONVERSATION STARTER

Encourage your child to think about the qualities listed in the "Putting It Into Practice" section on the previous page. Discuss which ones your kids feel are strengths in their lives and which ones they need to develop more fully.

Teenage Children *(AGES 14-COLLEGE)*

Rachel: As your kids become teenagers and have more independence, it's time to introduce the concept of giving of their time and talents, as well as their money. Encourage them to find ways they can serve by doing things they already enjoy and are good at. In the Ramsey house, all three kids were expected to participate in some kind of mission trip, and all three of us had life-changing, mind-blowing experiences as a result. There's no better way to pop the American middle-class bubble than to send your child on a mission trip to a struggling part of the world. Most of the time teens come back totally changed people.

WATCH: AGES 14–COLLEGE DEEP DIVE

Join Rachel and Dave as they discuss ways teenagers can learn to give of themselves that go way beyond the money in their wallets.

PUTTING IT INTO PRACTICE

Spend some time going through Genesis 12:2–3 with your teenagers. Talk about how Abraham was a blessing to others and how we should bless others as well. Specifically talk through ways your teens can be a blessing with their money, with their time, and with their abilities.

FAMILY ACTIVITIES

Make sure you do the family activity found in the online experience, and be prepared to discuss it during the next class. Also remember to look for teachable moments throughout the week.

CONVERSATION STARTER

As you encourage your teen to develop a generous heart, talk about why God tells us to start by giving a tithe to our local church. Write your teen's thoughts in the space below.

The Joy of Giving

Dave often says that giving is the most fun you can have with money. Take a few minutes to share a little bit of your story by answering the following questions.

When did you first begin to understand the importance of being generous? Who helped you understand that better?

Talk about a time when you have been on the receiving end of someone else's generosity.

Have you ever missed a chance to be generous and regretted it later? How can you be sure not to miss those chances now?

REFLECTION

Think about your kids' talents and abilities. How could they use those to become generous toward others?

If you were going to set a generosity goal—a God-sized giving challenge where you could use the blessings God has given you to bless someone else—what would it be? Why?

NEXT WEEK

Be prepared to discuss what you've learned from this week's lesson or to share your experiences with teachable moments this week.

The borrower is slave to the lender

–PROVERBS 22:7 (NIV)

5 *Lesson Five*

DEBT AND HONESTY

We all want our kids to have a secure future and a character of honesty. That's why the subject of debt is so important. Debt, by nature, creates roadblocks to a secure future, and it's built on a foundation of lies.

Debt IS a Four-Letter Word

This week, Rachel and Dave dig into a topic that our kids absolutely must understand: debt. They will cover:

- What debt really means
- What the Bible has to say about debt
- How debt is built on a foundation of lies

• • •

Dave: Normal in America is broke. So if you do normal behaviors, you will be broke, and if your kids are financially normal, they will be broke.

Examine the mythology believed and spread by normal people. Normal people say things like: "You must build your credit." "You will always have a car payment." "You can't be a student without a student loan." And, of course, "You will always have a mortgage." This is the lingo, the language, of normal people—people who live paycheck to paycheck and struggle through life.

Not me. As for me and my house, we have declared war on normal.

REFLECTION  QUESTION

Take about two minutes to write your answer to the following question.

No one wants to be broke, and yet normal people in America are. Why do you think that so many people believe that debt is okay?

Rachel: I don't know anyone who would come right out and say, "I absolutely love debt! I'm so glad I owe tens of thousands of dollars to the bank! I'm so blessed!"

No, that'd be crazy. But I guarantee that your child will hear common lies about debt all the time, and they'll probably start hearing them sooner than you think.

Your kids are growing up in the most indebted generation in history. The great news for you is that you can prepare your child to avoid this financial mess. If you still have kids living at home, then you are in the perfect position to teach them the behaviors that will keep them out of debt and set them up to win for life.

WATCH: PART 1 14 minutes

It's time to hear more from Rachel about the dangers of debt. Take a few minutes to watch the first part of Lesson Five.

Video Notes and Thoughts:

REFLECTION  QUESTION

Take about two minutes to write your answer to the following question.

What are some truths about debt that you really want your kids to believe?

"DEBT IS A THIEF. IT STEALS MONEY AND PEACE OF MIND.

—Rachel Cruze

Dave: I discovered this idea of debt-free living through the lens of my faith. When we hit bottom, I began studying the Bible and found that it had pretty clear principles for handling money. The easiest, yet hardest, principle I found was debt is never a good thing. Nowhere in Scripture is debt mentioned in a positive light.

The Bible says over and over that if you purposely put yourself in debt, you are a fool. It also says that debt makes you a slave and debt is a curse. So I have concluded that, biblically speaking, debt is stupid.

From that perspective, once I learned that debt isn't biblical, it made *not* borrowing money an easy decision—it was an act of faith. At the same time, not borrowing money was the hardest decision I have made.

WATCH: PART 2 9 minutes

Join Rachel as she talks about the foundation of deception on which debt is built and how honesty can help teens see through the myths.

Video Notes and Thoughts:

REFLECTION  QUESTION

Take about two minutes to write your answer to the following question.

What are some consequences—both good and bad—you have experienced because of your approach to debt?

SIGN IN TO SMARTMONEYSMARTKIDS.COM

Join Rachel and Dave as they discuss some practical ways to change your family tree by avoiding debt.

Deep Dives

There's no such thing as "good debt," but that doesn't stop people from falling into its trap each day. Today's Deep Dives section gives you some tips on how to help your kids avoid the popular lies related to debt so they can win in life. It includes videos and activities that are relevant to your kids' ages.

Rachel: As we walk through some of the big misconceptions about debt, I want to remind you of something. I said earlier that I like to view my dad as the emergency surgeon, but I'm the preventative medicine. That's exactly what we're doing here: preventative medicine.

If your child can stay away from debt for life, she can completely avoid most of the financial nightmares that this generation is facing, and she will never experience the stress of owing anything to anyone. That's what preventative medicine is all about.

REFLECTION  QUESTION

Take about two minutes to write your responses to the following questions.

Think about each of your kids. Which one(s) will struggle most with staying out of debt? Which one(s) will have an easier time living debt free?

WATCH: DEEP DIVE OVERVIEW

Join Rachel and Dave as they explain how spenders and savers respond to debt differently—and why they both need to steer clear of it.

APPLICATION: DEEP DIVES

Age-Specific Application

The next three pages contain age-specific videos and activities.
Please skip to the section(s) that best fits your family.

Younger Children *(AGES 3-5)*

Rachel: If you as the parent have these conversations with your kids and show them how to live a debt-free life, you have given them a tremendous gift. Most parents today don't think to talk to their kids about debt, and some have even bought into the lie so much that they teach their kids to believe it too. That's how families stay in debt generation after generation. But you can choose a different path, one that your children will thank you for for the rest of their lives.

WATCH: AGES 3–5 DEEP DIVE

Join Rachel and Dave as they talk about how the message of debt has worked its way into the world of even our preschoolers.

PUTTING IT INTO PRACTICE

When you're out shopping, show your kids the price of multiple items. Talk about how the numbers relate to money—and that some things cost more than others. Emphasize that you can't buy something unless you have the money for it.

FAMILY ACTIVITIES

Make sure you do the family activity found in the online experience, and be prepared to discuss it during the next class. Also remember to look for teachable moments throughout the week.

CONVERSATION STARTER

Talk to your child about the difference between needs and wants. Ask: What should we spend money on first? *Write the highlights of this conversation in the space below.*

Older Children *(AGES 6–13)*

Rachel: Love them or hate them, you at least have to recognize what an amazing job the credit card industry has done in marketing their products to us. They figured out that parents have just about all the cards they can fit in their wallets, so they had to change tactics.

That's when they started using "kiddie branding." Why do banks and credit card companies spend money putting their logo in front of an eight-year-old? Because ten years later, when that kid gets three credit card offers in the mail on the first day of college, she'll already know which one she wants.

You've got to teach your children to recognize these messages whenever you watch a show together or pick out a toy. Be on guard with your kids.

WATCH: AGES 6–13 DEEP DIVE

Join Rachel and Dave as they discuss ways parents can teach their older kids to develop discernment and recognize the myths of marketing.

PUTTING IT INTO PRACTICE

Help your kids recognize when the media is selling debt. For example, point out credit card commercials on TV or car financing ads in newspapers. Talk about how they make debt look fun and normal even though debt is really a trap.

FAMILY ACTIVITIES

Make sure you do the family activity found in the online experience, and be prepared to discuss it during the next class. Also remember to look for teachable moments throughout the week.

CONVERSATION STARTER

Remind your child that the Bible never has anything good to say about debt. In fact, the Bible says the borrower is slave to the lender. Ask some questions like these: How much freedom does a slave have? How can being a slave to debt steal your freedom? *Write your child's responses to this conversation in the space below.*

APPLICATION: DEEP DIVES

Teenage Children *(AGES 14-COLLEGE)*

Rachel: Student loans are a roadblock to this generation. Altogether, there is roughly $1 trillion in total outstanding student loan debt in the United States today, and student loans have recently surpassed credit cards in total debt owed.

Graduates will carry those loans around with them for years or even decades. They can't even escape them through bankruptcy because federally backed student loans are not eliminated in a bankruptcy.

The short-term gain of student loans doesn't even compare to the long-term pain your student could end up with. There's no doubt: This is a generational crisis, and, as a parent, you need to be ready.

WATCH: AGES 14–COLLEGE DEEP DIVE

Join Rachel and Dave as they discuss dangerous debts that are sidetracking many teens today: credit cards, car loans, and student loans.

PUTTING IT INTO PRACTICE

Along with college, cars are another big topic for teens. But before they can drive away, they've got to figure out how much it all costs. Talk with your teen about making a plan.

They should set a date and budget for a reliable used car, come up with at least three car options within that budget, and determine how much they'll need to save each month to reach their goal. Encourage them to look online for any information they'll need to make an intelligent decision.

FAMILY ACTIVITIES

Make sure you do the family activity found in the online experience, and be prepared to discuss it during the next class. Also remember to look for teachable moments throughout the week.

CONVERSATION STARTER

Review the lies Rachel talked about in this lesson with your teen. Ask: Which ones do you hear most often? Which ones are you most tempted to believe? *Write their responses in the space below.*

Breaking the Chains of Debt

Debt is normal, but your goal should be complete and total weirdness. Reflect on the impact debt has had on your life, then tell a bit of your story by answering the following questions.

What is the very first thing you remember going into debt for? About how much was it? How long did it take to pay it off?

What kinds of things has debt kept you from doing?

What attitude did your parents have about debt? How did that affect the way you viewed debt when you were younger?

Do you think it's realistic for your kids to avoid going into debt their entire lives? Why or why not?

What blessings do you see in the lives of people who choose to avoid debt? How does that affect your take on going into debt?

NEXT WEEK

Be prepared to discuss what you've learned from this week's lesson or to share your experiences with teachable moments this week.

I have learned in whatever state I am, to be content

–PHILIPPIANS 4:11

6

Lesson Six

CONTENTMENT AND GRATITUDE

Charles Spurgeon was right when he said, "If you are not content with what you have, you would not be satisfied if it were doubled." Teaching our kids to be humble, grateful, and content is one of the most important things we can do to set them up for a lifetime of success.

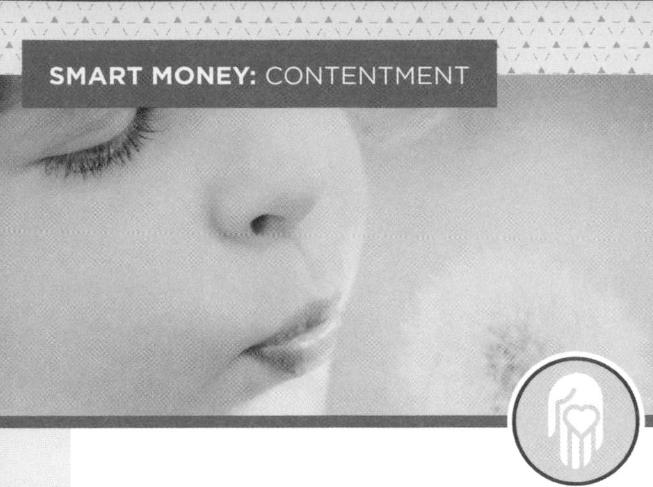

The War for Your Child's Heart

This week, Rachel and Dave talk about the powerful principles of humility, gratitude, and contentment, including:

- How contentment isn't a money issue—it's a heart issue
- Why it's important for your kids to embrace gratitude
- Why contentment really isn't a destination, but a manner of travel

• • •

Dave: We live in the most marketed-to culture in the history of the world. We are hit by more advertising impressions in a few hours than previous generations experienced in an entire year. I'm not against marketing, but we must understand that the very purpose of marketing is to make us feel discontent with our lives.

If you want to raise money-smart kids, you have to raise kids who are content. Contentment is the best insurance policy that your kids will win with money as adults. Content people may not have the best of everything, but they make the best of everything. That is who you want your children to be.

Take about two minutes to write your answer to the following question.

What are some real ways you see marketing making an impact on your kid's level of contentment?

Dave: Some of my favorite films are war movies. I like to see a group of people fighting for something they actually care about—something worth fighting for. The goal is clear, and the enemy is in sight. There's a passion and conviction in those stories you rarely see anywhere else.

When the stakes are high and the cause is just, good men and women are inspired to go to war. They are willing to stand up and fight to the finish, if that's what it takes. Well, I'm going to let you in on a little secret: If you are raising children in North America today, you are at war.

WATCH: PART 1 15 minutes

It's time to hear from Rachel and Dave about the value of nurturing contentment in your life—and in the life of your child. Take a few minutes to watch the first part of Lesson Six.

Video Notes and Thoughts:

REFLECTION QUESTION

Take about two minutes to write your answers to the following questions.

Would you describe yourself as content? Why or why not?

"CONTENTMENT IS NOT A DESTINATION. IT'S THE MANNER OF TRAVEL.

—Rachel Cruze

Rachel: I want you to see the trail that runs from giving to humility to gratitude to contentment. It's a progression that leads your child out of the land of discontentment and toward an incredible life of joy and freedom. When your child is focused on meeting the real *needs* of others through giving, it becomes harder and harder for him to focus on his *wants*.

WATCH: PART 2 6 minutes

Join Rachel as she talks about how contentment helps kids flourish financially and spiritually.

Video Notes and Thoughts:

REFLECTION  QUESTION

Take about two minutes to write your answer to the following question.

Rachel reminded us how important it is to remember that God owns it all. What's one thing you could start doing to help you and your kids remember this on a daily basis?

WATCH: PART 3 9 minutes

As you wrap up today's lesson and the six weeks of the Smart Money Smart Kids *study, watch the concluding video clip from Rachel and Dave.*

SIGN IN TO SMARTMONEYSMARTKIDS.COM

Join Rachel and Dave as they discuss the signs of discontentment and what that means for raising money-smart kids.

Deep Dives

Content people make the best of everything, but how do you teach your kids contentment? Today's Deep Dives section gives you some ideas for helping your kids develop an attitude of gratitude. It also includes videos and activities that are relevant to their ages.

Rachel: As giving becomes a natural part of your child's character, you'll see his whole perspective change. It's hard for discontentment to take root in a heart filled with humility.

In the same way, it's almost impossible for selfishness to flourish in the heart of a giver. With every act of giving, your child is taking a stand against discontentment. It's like he's saying, "I not only have enough for me, but I have enough to share with you." That's the fertile ground of contentment.

REFLECTION  QUESTION

Take about two minutes to write your answers to the following questions.

Think about each of your kids. Which signs of discontentment do you see at work in their lives? How can you help them overcome those struggles?

WATCH: DEEP DIVE OVERVIEW

Join Rachel and Dave as they offer some practical advice for instilling contentment into the lives of your children.

Age-Specific Application

The next three pages contain age-specific videos and activities. **Please skip to the section(s) that best fits your family.**

Younger Children *(AGES 3-5)*

Dave: Gratitude is really, really attractive. A child who is genuinely grateful makes you want to do anything for her, and that is true of adults as well. As parents, we've all experienced those wonderful, sweet, humbling moments when our children look at us with eyes filled with gratitude for something we've done for them. At that moment, they are the most beautiful, most precious children they could ever be. And, sadly, most of us have had the opposite experience—seeing a child open a present and act ungrateful. There are few things uglier than that.

WATCH: AGES 3–5 DEEP DIVE

Join Rachel and Dave as they share how contentment begins to take root when your kids understand that God owns it all.

PUTTING IT INTO PRACTICE

Take your kids outside for a reminder that God made it all, owns it all, and cares for it all.

Have them look for something God made that they can see, something God made that they can smell, something God made that they can hear, and something God made that they can touch.

FAMILY ACTIVITIES

Be sure to do the family activity found in the online experience, and be prepared to discuss it during the next class. Be sure you're also looking for teachable moments throughout the week.

CONVERSATION STARTER

Now is the time to start teaching your child that God owns everything. Talk to your child about how all the stuff we have is really His and how we need to take care of the things He gives us. Write the highlights from this conversation in the space below.

Older Children *(AGES 6-13)*

Dave: We have established that there is a war in our culture for the hearts of our children. Left unchecked, the cultural forces will steal your children's hearts and make them believe the lie that life consists of the stuff or experiences we buy. My goal here is to stir you up—to get you mad enough to go to war with that culture and win your child's heart to contentment.

WATCH: AGES 6–13 DEEP DIVE

Join Rachel and Dave as they discuss how avoiding comparisons can be a great step toward overcoming discontentment.

PUTTING IT INTO PRACTICE

Plan a family game night. As you play the game, remind your kids that we can learn a lot about being content when we celebrate the good things that happen to others. Share Romans 12:15 and encourage them to be excited when they hear good news—no matter whose good news it is.

FAMILY ACTIVITIES

Make sure you do the family activity found in the online experience, and be prepared to discuss it during the next class. Also remember to look for teachable moments throughout the week.

CONVERSATION STARTER

Ask your children who they might be tempted to compare themselves to. Talk about how God wants us to be content with the people He has made us to be—and how comparing ourselves to others makes that harder. Write the key points of this conversation in the space below.

Teenage Children *(AGES 14-COLLEGE)*

Dave: As parents, of course we don't want to intentionally raise children who are so shallow that they define themselves by a purchase or an item. So how do we prevent it in the midst of a culture where it is virtually the norm? By being careful to celebrate the accomplishments and character qualities that enabled them to make the purchase, you are reminding your children that they are not defined by the abundance of their possessions.

Contentment isn't a destination; it's not somewhere you're leaving from, and it isn't somewhere you're heading to. Contentment is a manner of traveling. It's an attitude of peace and joy where you are, even while you are working to be somewhere else.

WATCH: AGES 14–COLLEGE DEEP DIVE

Join Rachel and Dave as they discuss how teens can find their identities in contentment instead of what they see on social media or reality TV.

PUTTING IT INTO PRACTICE

Use the scale below to measure how your kids feel about themselves. Pick a number for each of your kids.

1 2 3 4 5 6 7 8 9 10

VERY UNCOMFORTABLE — SUPER CONFIDENT

What connections do you see between your kids' attitude of gratitude and where they land on the scale? What can you do to help your kids be both confident and content?

FAMILY ACTIVITIES

Make sure you do the family activity found in the online experience, and be prepared to discuss it during the next class. Also remember to look for teachable moments throughout the week.

CONVERSATION STARTER

Ask your teen these questions: How do you think God feels about you? What makes it hard to accept how much He loves and cares about you? *Write their responses in the space below.*

A Life of Contentment

Living a life of contentment and gratitude is possible for all of us. Think back on the twists and turns of your life up to this point. Take a few minutes to tell a little bit of your story by answering the following questions.

What person in your life has truly modeled contentment?

What are some places in your life where you find yourself having to fight off discontentment?

What changes in your life have helped you to become more content? What convinced you to make those changes?

REFLECTION

What are the things in your life that you are most grateful for?

Why is it so important to you that your kids become grateful and content adults?

Congrats!

You did it! You watched the videos. You answered the questions. You bounced ideas off other parents. Most important, you've taken a big step toward making a difference in how your kids understand money!

Great job!

Of course, you already know that the job of parenting never really ends. Your commitment to join this *Smart Money Smart Kids* class is more like a starter's gun than a finish line. So our congratulations also have to come with a challenge: *Don't stop now!*

You've soaked in a ton of information and ideas over the last six weeks, and you might feel a little overwhelmed at the moment. That's okay. Just remember that you've got the tools to change your family tree, and you can build a powerful legacy that will touch generations to come. There's only one thing left to do . . .

Keep moving forward!

Student Budget

Yes, this budget form has a lot of lines and blanks.
But that's okay. We do that so we can list practically every expense imaginable on this form to prevent you from forgetting something. Don't expect to put something on every line. Just use the ones that are relevant to your specific situation.

Step 1

Write your monthly income in the box at the top (**A**), including any money your parents give you. This is the amount you have to spend for the month. Pretty simple, right?

Step 2

At the bottom of the form, write your income in the Income box (**B**).

Step 3

Within each category, like Recreation, there are items like Movie and Sporting Event. Start at the top and work your way down, filling out the Budgeted column (**C**) first. Add up each subcategory and put that number in the Total box (**D**).

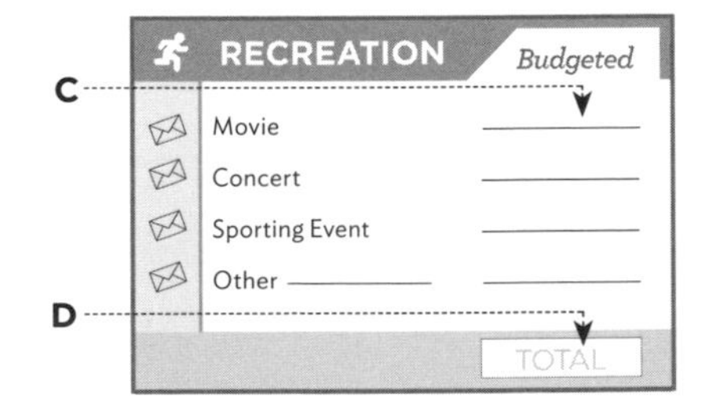

Step 4

Go through the form and add up all of the category Total boxes (**D**). Write that grand total in the Outgo box (**E**). That's how much you spend every month. The goal is to spend every dollar you make, but no more. So if your Outgo is greater than your Income, you need to bring down the budgeted amount on some items. If your Outgo is less than your Income, you need to increase the amount in some area like College Savings or Restaurants.

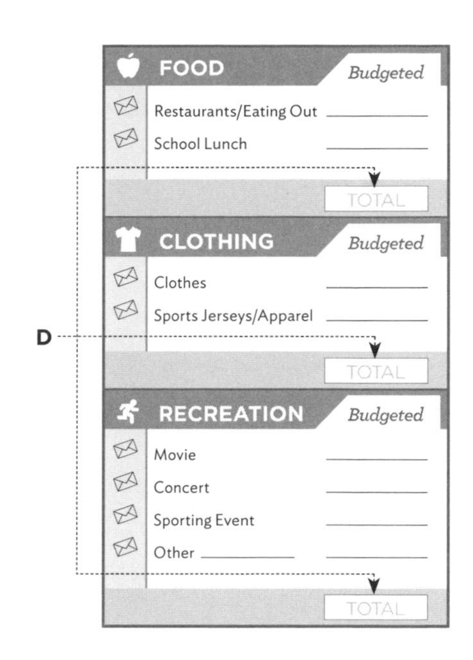

Step 5

Once your Outgo is the same as your Income, write a zero in the Zero box at the bottom (**F**). You're done!

Student Budget

INCOME

Add up budgeted column & enter here

GIVING

	Budgeted
Tithe	______
Charity	______
	TOTAL

SAVING

	Budgeted
Emergency Fund	______
College	______
Car & Repairs	______
Computer	______
Other ______	______
	TOTAL

FOOD

	Budgeted
Restaurants/Eating Out	______
School Lunch/Vending Machine	______
	TOTAL

CLOTHING

	Budgeted
Clothes	______
Sports Jerseys/Apparel	______
	TOTAL

These icons represent good options for cash envelopes

TRANSPORTATION	*Budgeted*
Gas	______
Car Insurance	______
Oil Change	______
License & Taxes	______
	TOTAL

PERSONAL	*Budgeted*
Cosmetics/Hair Care	______
Music/Technology	______
Gifts	______
Pocket Money	______
Cell Phone	______
Other ______	______
	TOTAL

RECREATION	*Budgeted*
Movie	______
Concert	______
Sporting Event	______
Other ______	______
	TOTAL

INCOME - OUTGO = ZERO

Add up totals from each category

Remember—The goal is to get this number to zero

Upcoming Expenses

How do you eat an elephant? One bite at a time.

You'll usually have a few big expenses, like a spring break trip, club dues, sports or music equipment and prom, throughout the year. These things can be budget busters if you don't plan ahead. Use this form to break down those upcoming expenses into bite-sized chunks for your monthly budget.

ITEM	NEEDED ÷	MONTHS =	BUDGET
A	B	C	D

Step 1

The Item column (**A**) lists common big expenses that you might need to plan for. If something is missing, fill it in as Other.

Step 2

For the items that apply to you, write how much money you'll need for that expense in the Needed column (**B**). Then figure out how many months you have to save up for that item, and write that in the Months column (**C**).

For example, let's say it's June and you want to spend $120 on Christmas presents for your friends this year. You'd need $120 by December, and you have six months to save.

Step 3

Now, for each item, divide the Needed amount by the Months you have. Write that in the Budget column (**D**).

So for Christmas, $120 divided by six months is $20 a month. That's how much you need to save each month to have $120 in time for Christmas. Now you can just put that $20 per month item on your monthly budget in the Savings category.

How much cash will you need? How many months do you have? Monthly amount for your student budget

ITEM	NEEDED ÷	MONTHS =	BUDGET
Homecoming	____	____	____
School Club	____	____	____
Sports Fees	____	____	____
Christmas	____	____	____
Valentine's Day	____	____	____
Spring Break	____	____	____
Anniversary	____	____	____
Prom	____	____	____
Other ____	____	____	____
____	____	____	____
____	____	____	____
____	____	____	____
____	____	____	____
____	____	____	____
____	____	____	____
____	____	____	____

Memories and Milestones

Memories and Milestones

Memories and Milestones

Memories and Milestones